Say the sounds and blend them together to read the words. (Letters in faint type are silent letters and do not make a sound in the word.)

farm

house

Say the word *goat* and listen out for the sounds: *goat* – /g-oa-t/. (There is one sound dot underneath the goat for each sound in the word.)

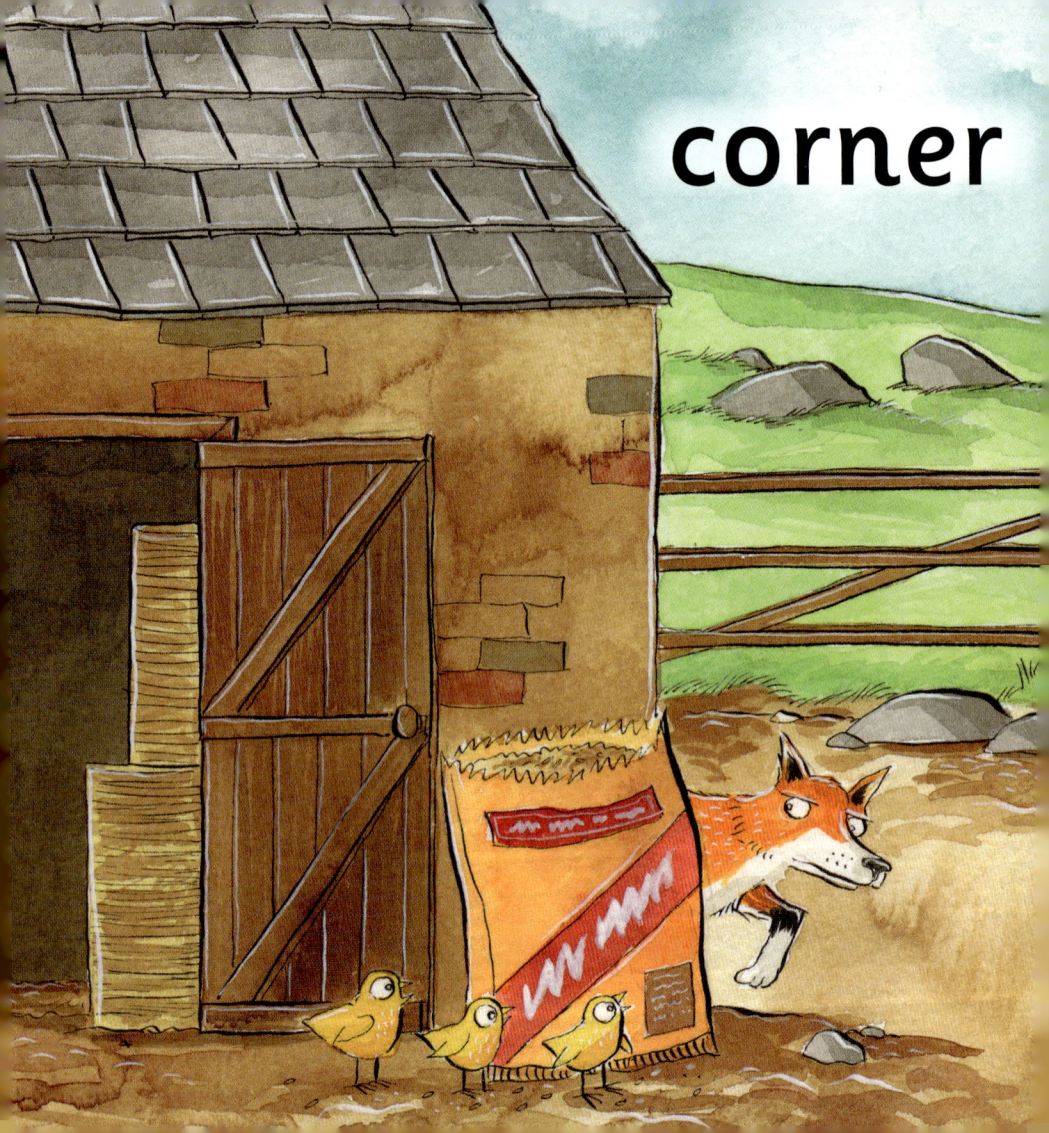